Published by Danilo Promotions Ltd. Unit 3, The io Centre,
Lea Road, Waltham Abbey, EN9 1AS, England.
Enquiries: **info@danilo.com**
For all other information: **www.danilo.com**
Printed in South Korea.

PERSONAL INFORMATION

Name:

Address:

Home Telephone:

Mobile:

Email:

Business Address:

Work Telephone:

Work Email:

Car Registration:

Driving Licence:

Insurance Number:

Passport Number:

Doctor:

Doctor Telephone:

Blood Group:

Allergies:

In case of an emergency please contact:

Name:

Address:

Telephone:

CONTACT INFORMATION

Name:

Address / Telephone:

Name:

Address / Telephone:

Name:

Address / Telephone:

Name:

Address / Telephone:

Name:

Address / Telephone:

Name:

Address / Telephone:

CONTACT INFORMATION

Name:

Address / Telephone:

Name:

Address / Telephone:

Name:

Address / Telephone:

Name:

Address / Telephone:

Name:

Address / Telephone:

Name:

Address / Telephone:

2023

JANUARY

WK	M	T	W	T	F	S	S
52							1
1	2	3	4	5	6	7	8
2	9	10	11	12	13	14	15
3	16	17	18	19	20	21	22
4	23	24	25	26	27	28	29
5	30	31					

FEBRUARY

WK	M	T	W	T	F	S	S
5			1	2	3	4	5
6	6	7	8	9	10	11	12
7	13	14	15	16	17	18	19
8	20	21	22	23	24	25	26
9	27	28					

MARCH

WK	M	T	W	T	F	S	S
9			1	2	3	4	5
10	6	7	8	9	10	11	12
11	13	14	15	16	17	18	19
12	20	21	22	23	24	25	26
13	27	28	29	30	31		

APRIL

WK	M	T	W	T	F	S	S
13						1	2
14	3	4	5	6	7	8	9
15	10	11	12	13	14	15	16
16	17	18	19	20	21	22	23
17	24	25	26	27	28	29	30

MAY

WK	M	T	W	T	F	S	S
18	1	2	3	4	5	6	7
19	8	9	10	11	12	13	14
20	15	16	17	18	19	20	21
21	22	23	24	25	26	27	28
22	29	30	31				

JUNE

WK	M	T	W	T	F	S	S
22				1	2	3	4
23	5	6	7	8	9	10	11
24	12	13	14	15	16	17	18
25	19	20	21	22	23	24	25
26	26	27	28	29	30		

JULY

WK	M	T	W	T	F	S	S
26						1	2
27	3	4	5	6	7	8	9
28	10	11	12	13	14	15	16
29	17	18	19	20	21	22	23
30	24	25	26	27	28	29	30
31	31						

AUGUST

WK	M	T	W	T	F	S	S
31		1	2	3	4	5	6
32	7	8	9	10	11	12	13
33	14	15	16	17	18	19	20
34	21	22	23	24	25	26	27
35	28	29	30	31			

SEPTEMBER

WK	M	T	W	T	F	S	S
35					1	2	3
36	4	5	6	7	8	9	10
37	11	12	13	14	15	16	17
38	18	19	20	21	22	23	24
39	25	26	27	28	29	30	

OCTOBER

WK	M	T	W	T	F	S	S
39							1
40	2	3	4	5	6	7	8
41	9	10	11	12	13	14	15
42	16	17	18	19	20	21	22
43	23	24	25	26	27	28	29
44	30	31					

NOVEMBER

WK	M	T	W	T	F	S	S
44			1	2	3	4	5
45	6	7	8	9	10	11	12
46	13	14	15	16	17	18	19
47	20	21	22	23	24	25	26
48	27	28	29	30			

DECEMBER

WK	M	T	W	T	F	S	S
48					1	2	3
49	4	5	6	7	8	9	10
50	11	12	13	14	15	16	17
51	18	19	20	21	22	23	24
52	25	26	27	28	29	30	31

2023 NOTABLE DATES

New Year's Day	Jan 1
New Year Holiday	Jan 2
Bank Holiday (Scotland)	Jan 3
Chinese New Year (Rabbit)	Jan 22
Valentine's Day	Feb 14
Shrove Tuesday	Feb 21
St. David's Day	Mar 1
St. Patrick's Day	Mar 17
Mothering Sunday (UK)	Mar 19
Ramadan Begins	Mar 22
Daylight Saving Time Starts	Mar 26
Passover Begins	Apr 5
Good Friday	Apr 7
Easter Sunday	Apr 9
Easter Monday	Apr 10
Earth Day	Apr 22
St. George's Day	Apr 23
Early May Bank Holiday	May 1
Spring Bank Holiday	May 29
Father's Day (UK)	Jun 18
Public Holiday (Northern Ireland)	Jul 12
Islamic New Year Begins	Jul 18
Summer Bank Holiday (Scotland)	Aug 7
Summer Bank Holiday (ENG, NIR, WAL)	Aug 28
Rosh Hashanah (Jewish New Year) Begins	Sept 15
International Day of Peace (United Nations)	Sept 21
Yom Kippur Begins	Sept 24
World Mental Health Day	Oct 10
Daylight Saving Time Ends	Oct 29
Halloween	Oct 31
Guy Fawkes Night	Nov 5
Diwali / Remembrance Sunday	Nov 12
St. Andrew's Day	Nov 30
Christmas Day	Dec 25
Boxing Day	Dec 26
New Year's Eve	Dec 31

2023 ADVANCE PLANNER

JANUARY

FEBRUARY

MARCH

APRIL

MAY

JUNE

2023 ADVANCE PLANNER

JULY

AUGUST

SEPTEMBER

OCTOBER

NOVEMBER

DECEMBER

26 MONDAY

---

27 TUESDAY

---

28 WEDNESDAY

---

29 THURSDAY

FRIDAY **30**

SATURDAY **31**

New Year's Eve

SUNDAY **1**

New Year's Day

KEEPING SCORE

Date:	Competition:
Opponents:	
Home ☐	Away ☐
Match score:	
Scorers:	
Player of the match:	

JANUARY

2   MONDAY

New Year Holiday

3   TUESDAY

Bank Holiday (Scotland)

4   WEDNESDAY

5   THURSDAY

FRIDAY **6**

SATURDAY **7**

SUNDAY **8**

KEEPING SCORE

Date: Competition:

Opponents:

Home ☐   Away ☐

Match score:

Scorers:

Player of the match:

9 MONDAY

10 TUESDAY

11 WEDNESDAY

12 THURSDAY

FRIDAY **13**

SATURDAY **14**

SUNDAY **15**

KEEPING SCORE

Date: Competition:

Opponents:

Home ☐   Away ☐

Match score:

Scorers:

Player of the match:

JANUARY

16 MONDAY

17 TUESDAY

18 WEDNESDAY

19 THURSDAY

FRIDAY **20**

SATURDAY **21**

SUNDAY **22**

Chinese New Year (Rabbit)

KEEPING SCORE

Date: Competition:

Opponents:

Home ☐   Away ☐

Match score:

Scorers:

Player of the match:

23 MONDAY

24 TUESDAY

25 WEDNESDAY

26 THURSDAY

FRIDAY **27**

SATURDAY **28**

SUNDAY **29**

KEEPING SCORE

Date: Competition:

Opponents:

Home ☐   Away ☐

Match score:

Scorers:

Player of the match:

30 MONDAY

31 TUESDAY

1 WEDNESDAY

2 THURSDAY

FRIDAY **3**

SATURDAY **4**

SUNDAY **5**

KEEPING SCORE

Date: Competition:

Opponents:

Home ☐   Away ☐

Match score:

Scorers:

Player of the match:

6   MONDAY

7   TUESDAY

8   WEDNESDAY

9   THURSDAY

FRIDAY **10**

SATURDAY **11**

SUNDAY **12**

KEEPING SCORE

Date: Competition:

Opponents:

Home ☐   Away ☐

Match score:

Scorers:

Player of the match:

FEBRUARY

13 MONDAY

14 TUESDAY

Valentine's Day

15 WEDNESDAY

16 THURSDAY

FRIDAY 17

SATURDAY 18

SUNDAY 19

KEEPING SCORE

Date: Competition:

Opponents:

Home ☐   Away ☐

Match score:

Scorers:

Player of the match:

FEBRUARY

20 MONDAY

21 TUESDAY

Shrove Tuesday

22 WEDNESDAY

23 THURSDAY

FRIDAY 24

SATURDAY 25

SUNDAY 26

KEEPING SCORE

Date: Competition:

Opponents:

Home ☐   Away ☐

Match score:

Scorers:

Player of the match:

27 MONDAY

28 TUESDAY

1 WEDNESDAY

St. David's Day

2 THURSDAY

FRIDAY **3**

SATURDAY **4**

SUNDAY **5**

KEEPING SCORE

Date: Competition:

Opponents:

Home ☐ Away ☐

Match score:

Scorers:

Player of the match:

MARCH

6 MONDAY

7 TUESDAY

8 WEDNESDAY

9 THURSDAY

MARCH

FRIDAY **10**

SATURDAY **11**

SUNDAY **12**

KEEPING SCORE

Date: Competition:

Opponents:

Home ☐   Away ☐

Match score:

Scorers:

Player of the match:

13 MONDAY

14 TUESDAY

15 WEDNESDAY

16 THURSDAY

FRIDAY **17**

St. Patrick's Day

SATURDAY **18**

SUNDAY **19**

Mothering Sunday (UK)

KEEPING SCORE

Date:	Competition:
Opponents:	
Home ☐	Away ☐
Match score:	
Scorers:	
Player of the match:	

MARCH

20 MONDAY

21 TUESDAY

22 WEDNESDAY

Ramadan Begins

23 THURSDAY

FRIDAY **24**

SATURDAY **25**

SUNDAY **26**

Daylight Saving Time Starts

KEEPING SCORE

Date:	Competition:
Opponents:	
Home ☐	Away ☐
Match score:	
Scorers:	
Player of the match:	

MARCH

27 MONDAY

28 TUESDAY

29 WEDNESDAY

30 THURSDAY

FRIDAY **31**

SATURDAY **1**

SUNDAY **2**

KEEPING SCORE

Date: Competition:

Opponents:

Home ☐   Away ☐

Match score:

Scorers:

Player of the match:

3 MONDAY

4 TUESDAY

5 WEDNESDAY

Passover Begins

6 THURSDAY

FRIDAY **7**

Good Friday

SATURDAY **8**

SUNDAY **9**

Easter Sunday

KEEPING SCORE

Date: Competition:

Opponents:

Home ☐   Away ☐

Match score:

Scorers:

Player of the match:

APRIL

10 MONDAY

Easter Monday

11 TUESDAY

12 WEDNESDAY

13 THURSDAY

FRIDAY 14

SATURDAY 15

SUNDAY 16

KEEPING SCORE

Date: Competition:

Opponents:

Home ☐   Away ☐

Match score:

Scorers:

Player of the match:

APRIL

17 MONDAY

18 TUESDAY

19 WEDNESDAY

20 THURSDAY

FRIDAY **21**

SATURDAY **22**

Earth Day

SUNDAY **23**

St. George's Day

KEEPING SCORE

Date:	Competition:

Opponents:

Home ☐	Away ☐	

Match score:

Scorers:

Player of the match:

24 MONDAY

25 TUESDAY

26 WEDNESDAY

27 THURSDAY

FRIDAY 28

SATURDAY 29

SUNDAY 30

KEEPING SCORE

Date: Competition:

Opponents:

Home ☐   Away ☐

Match score:

Scorers:

Player of the match:

MAY

1 MONDAY

Early May Bank Holiday

2 TUESDAY

3 WEDNESDAY

4 THURSDAY

FRIDAY **5**

SATURDAY **6**

SUNDAY **7**

KEEPING SCORE

Date: Competition:

Opponents:

Home ☐   Away ☐

Match score:

Scorers:

Player of the match:

MAY

8 MONDAY

9 TUESDAY

10 WEDNESDAY

11 THURSDAY

FRIDAY **12**

SATURDAY **13**

SUNDAY **14**

KEEPING SCORE

Date: Competition:

Opponents:

Home ☐   Away ☐

Match score:

Scorers:

Player of the match:

15 MONDAY

16 TUESDAY

17 WEDNESDAY

18 THURSDAY

FRIDAY **19**

SATURDAY **20**

SUNDAY **21**

KEEPING SCORE

Date: Competition:

Opponents:

Home ☐ Away ☐

Match score:

Scorers:

Player of the match:

22 MONDAY

23 TUESDAY

24 WEDNESDAY

25 THURSDAY

FRIDAY **26**

SATURDAY **27**

SUNDAY **28**

KEEPING SCORE

Date: Competition:

Opponents:

Home ☐   Away ☐

Match score:

Scorers:

Player of the match:

29 MONDAY

Spring Bank Holiday

30 TUESDAY

31 WEDNESDAY

1 THURSDAY

FRIDAY **2**

SATURDAY **3**

SUNDAY **4**

KEEPING SCORE

Date: Competition:

Opponents:

Home ☐   Away ☐

Match score:

Scorers:

Player of the match:

JUNE

5   MONDAY

6   TUESDAY

7   WEDNESDAY

8   THURSDAY

FRIDAY **9**

SATURDAY **10**

SUNDAY **11**

KEEPING SCORE

Date: Competition:

Opponents:

Home ☐   Away ☐

Match score:

Scorers:

Player of the match:

JUNE

12 MONDAY

13 TUESDAY

14 WEDNESDAY

15 THURSDAY

FRIDAY 16

SATURDAY 17

SUNDAY 18

Father's Day (UK)

KEEPING SCORE

Date: Competition:

Opponents:

Home ☐   Away ☐

Match score:

Scorers:

Player of the match:

JUNE

19 MONDAY

20 TUESDAY

21 WEDNESDAY

22 THURSDAY

FRIDAY **23**

SATURDAY **24**

SUNDAY **25**

KEEPING SCORE

Date: Competition:

Opponents:

Home ☐ Away ☐

Match score:

Scorers:

Player of the match:

JUNE

26 MONDAY

27 TUESDAY

28 WEDNESDAY

29 THURSDAY

FRIDAY 30

SATURDAY 1

SUNDAY 2

KEEPING SCORE

Date:	Competition:

Opponents:

Home	☐	Away	☐

Match score:

Scorers:

Player of the match:

3 MONDAY

4 TUESDAY

5 WEDNESDAY

6 THURSDAY

FRIDAY   **7**

SATURDAY   **8**

SUNDAY   **9**

KEEPING SCORE

Date: Competition:

Opponents:

Home ☐   Away ☐

Match score:

Scorers:

Player of the match:

JULY

10 MONDAY

11 TUESDAY

12 WEDNESDAY

Public Holiday (Northern Ireland)

13 THURSDAY

FRIDAY 14

SATURDAY 15

SUNDAY 16

KEEPING SCORE

Date: Competition:

Opponents:

Home ☐   Away ☐

Match score:

Scorers:

Player of the match:

JULY

17 MONDAY

18 TUESDAY

Islamic New Year Begins

19 WEDNESDAY

20 THURSDAY

FRIDAY **21**

SATURDAY **22**

SUNDAY **23**

KEEPING SCORE

Date: Competition:

Opponents:

Home ☐   Away ☐

Match score:

Scorers:

Player of the match:

JULY

24 MONDAY

25 TUESDAY

26 WEDNESDAY

27 THURSDAY

FRIDAY **28**

SATURDAY **29**

SUNDAY **30**

KEEPING SCORE

Date: Competition:

Opponents:

Home ☐   Away ☐

Match score:

Scorers:

Player of the match:

31 MONDAY

1 TUESDAY

2 WEDNESDAY

3 THURSDAY

FRIDAY   **4**

SATURDAY   **5**

SUNDAY   **6**

KEEPING SCORE

Date:	Competition:
Opponents:	
Home ☐	Away ☐
Match score:	
Scorers:	
Player of the match:	

AUGUST

7 MONDAY

Summer Bank Holiday (Scotland)

8 TUESDAY

9 WEDNESDAY

10 THURSDAY

FRIDAY 11

SATURDAY 12

SUNDAY 13

KEEPING SCORE

Date: Competition:

Opponents:

Home ☐   Away ☐

Match score:

Scorers:

Player of the match:

AUGUST

14 MONDAY

15 TUESDAY

16 WEDNESDAY

17 THURSDAY

FRIDAY **18**

SATURDAY **19**

SUNDAY **20**

KEEPING SCORE

Date: Competition:

Opponents:

Home ☐   Away ☐

Match score:

Scorers:

Player of the match:

21 MONDAY

22 TUESDAY

23 WEDNESDAY

24 THURSDAY

FRIDAY 25

SATURDAY 26

SUNDAY 27

KEEPING SCORE

Date:		Competition:

Opponents:

Home ☐	Away ☐

Match score:

Scorers:

Player of the match:

AUGUST

28 MONDAY

Summer Bank Holiday (ENG, NIR, WAL)

29 TUESDAY

30 WEDNESDAY

31 THURSDAY

FRIDAY **1**

SATURDAY **2**

SUNDAY **3**

KEEPING SCORE

Date: Competition:

Opponents:

Home ☐ Away ☐

Match score:

Scorers:

Player of the match:

SEPTEMBER

4 MONDAY

5 TUESDAY

6 WEDNESDAY

7 THURSDAY

FRIDAY **8**

SATURDAY **9**

SUNDAY **10**

KEEPING SCORE

Date: Competition:

Opponents:

Home ☐   Away ☐

Match score:

Scorers:

Player of the match:

SEPTEMBER

11 MONDAY

12 TUESDAY

13 WEDNESDAY

14 THURSDAY

FRIDAY 15

Rosh Hashanah (Jewish New Year) Begins

SATURDAY 16

SUNDAY 17

KEEPING SCORE

Date:	Competition:
Opponents:	
Home ☐	Away ☐
Match score:	
Scorers:	
Player of the match:	

SEPTEMBER

18 MONDAY

19 TUESDAY

20 WEDNESDAY

21 THURSDAY

International Day of Peace (United Nations)

FRIDAY **22**

SATURDAY **23**

SUNDAY **24**

Yom Kippur Begins

KEEPING SCORE

Date: Competition:

Opponents:

Home ☐   Away ☐

Match score:

Scorers:

Player of the match:

SEPTEMBER

25 MONDAY

26 TUESDAY

27 WEDNESDAY

28 THURSDAY

FRIDAY **29**

SATURDAY **30**

SUNDAY **1**

KEEPING SCORE

Date:	Competition:
Opponents:	
Home ☐	Away ☐
Match score:	
Scorers:	
Player of the match:	

OCTOBER

2 MONDAY

3 TUESDAY

4 WEDNESDAY

5 THURSDAY

FRIDAY 6

SATURDAY 7

SUNDAY 8

KEEPING SCORE

Date: _____   Competition: _____

Opponents: _____

Home ☐   Away ☐

Match score: _____

Scorers: _____

Player of the match: _____

OCTOBER

9 MONDAY

10 TUESDAY

World Mental Health Day

11 WEDNESDAY

12 THURSDAY

FRIDAY **13**

SATURDAY **14**

SUNDAY **15**

KEEPING SCORE

Date: Competition:

Opponents:

Home ☐ Away ☐

Match score:

Scorers:

Player of the match:

OCTOBER

16 MONDAY

17 TUESDAY

18 WEDNESDAY

19 THURSDAY

FRIDAY **20**

SATURDAY **21**

SUNDAY **22**

KEEPING SCORE

Date: Competition:

Opponents:

Home ☐   Away ☐

Match score:

Scorers:

Player of the match:

OCTOBER

23 MONDAY

24 TUESDAY

25 WEDNESDAY

26 THURSDAY

FRIDAY **27**

SATURDAY **28**

SUNDAY **29**

Daylight Saving Time Ends

KEEPING SCORE

Date: _____ Competition: _____

Opponents: _____

Home ☐   Away ☐

Match score: _____

Scorers: _____

Player of the match: _____

30 MONDAY

31 TUESDAY

Halloween

1 WEDNESDAY

2 THURSDAY

FRIDAY **3**

SATURDAY **4**

SUNDAY **5**

Guy Fawkes Night

KEEPING SCORE

Date: Competition:

Opponents:

Home ☐   Away ☐

Match score:

Scorers:

Player of the match:

NOVEMBER

6 MONDAY

7 TUESDAY

8 WEDNESDAY

9 THURSDAY

FRIDAY **10**

SATURDAY **11**

SUNDAY **12**

Diwali / Remembrance Sunday

KEEPING SCORE

Date: Competition:

Opponents:

Home ☐   Away ☐

Match score:

Scorers:

Player of the match:

NOVEMBER

13 MONDAY

14 TUESDAY

15 WEDNESDAY

16 THURSDAY

NOVEMBER

FRIDAY **17**

SATURDAY **18**

SUNDAY **19**

KEEPING SCORE

Date: Competition:

Opponents:

Home ☐   Away ☐

Match score:

Scorers:

Player of the match:

NOVEMBER

20 MONDAY

21 TUESDAY

22 WEDNESDAY

23 THURSDAY

FRIDAY 24

SATURDAY 25

SUNDAY 26

KEEPING SCORE

Date: Competition:

Opponents:

Home ☐   Away ☐

Match score:

Scorers:

Player of the match:

NOVEMBER

27 MONDAY

28 TUESDAY

29 WEDNESDAY

30 THURSDAY

St. Andrew's Day

FRIDAY **1**

SATURDAY **2**

SUNDAY **3**

KEEPING SCORE

Date: Competition:

Opponents:

Home ☐   Away ☐

Match score:

Scorers:

Player of the match:

DECEMBER

4 MONDAY

5 TUESDAY

6 WEDNESDAY

7 THURSDAY

FRIDAY **8**

SATURDAY **9**

SUNDAY **10**

KEEPING SCORE

Date: Competition:

Opponents:

Home ☐   Away ☐

Match score:

Scorers:

Player of the match:

DECEMBER

11 MONDAY

12 TUESDAY

13 WEDNESDAY

14 THURSDAY

FRIDAY **15**

SATURDAY **16**

SUNDAY **17**

KEEPING SCORE

Date: Competition:

Opponents:

Home ☐   Away ☐

Match score:

Scorers:

Player of the match:

DECEMBER

18 MONDAY

19 TUESDAY

20 WEDNESDAY

21 THURSDAY

FRIDAY **22**

SATURDAY **23**

SUNDAY **24**

KEEPING SCORE

Date: Competition:

Opponents:

Home ☐   Away ☐

Match score:

Scorers:

Player of the match:

DECEMBER

25 MONDAY

Christmas Day

26 TUESDAY

Boxing Day

27 WEDNESDAY

28 THURSDAY

FRIDAY **29**

SATURDAY **30**

SUNDAY **31**

New Year's Eve

KEEPING SCORE

Date: _____ Competition: _____

Opponents: _____

Home ☐   Away ☐

Match score: _____

Scorers: _____

Player of the match: _____

CONTACT INFORMATION

Name:

Address / Telephone:

Name:

Address / Telephone:

Name:

Address / Telephone:

Name:

Address / Telephone:

Name:

Address / Telephone:

Name:

Address / Telephone:

CONTACT INFORMATION

Name:

Address / Telephone:

Name:

Address / Telephone:

Name:

Address / Telephone:

Name:

Address / Telephone:

Name:

Address / Telephone:

Name:

Address / Telephone:

CONTACT INFORMATION

Name:

Address / Telephone:

Name:

Address / Telephone:

Name:

Address / Telephone:

Name:

Address / Telephone:

Name:

Address / Telephone:

Name:

Address / Telephone:

CONTACT INFORMATION

Name:

Address / Telephone:

Name:

Address / Telephone:

Name:

Address / Telephone:

Name:

Address / Telephone:

Name:

Address / Telephone:

Name:

Address / Telephone:

CONTACT INFORMATION

Name:

Address / Telephone:

Name:

Address / Telephone:

Name:

Address / Telephone:

Name:

Address / Telephone:

Name:

Address / Telephone:

Name:

Address / Telephone:

CONTACT INFORMATION

Name:

Address / Telephone:

Name:

Address / Telephone:

Name:

Address / Telephone:

Name:

Address / Telephone:

Name:

Address / Telephone:

Name:

Address / Telephone: